SUPER ③ SOAPS QUIZBOOK

CHRIS STACEY

BOXTREE

First published in Great Britain in 1991
by Boxtree Limited

Copyright © Boxtree Limited 1991

Front cover design: Anita Ruddell

ISBN 185283 604 0

Typeset by Cambrian Typesetters, Frimley, Surrey.
Printed and bound in Great Britain by
Cox & Wyman, Reading, Berkshire

A C.I.P. Catalogue for this book is available from the British Library

Contents

Introduction

Welcome to Supersoaps Quiz Book No 3 which I hope will provide more hours of puzzlement and fun for the whole family.

In this quiz book, I have included the soap of the 1990s, *Twin Peaks*, and the ever-popular *Prisoner Cell Block H*, along with dear old *Crossroads* which will always be special to me.

I would like to say thank you to everyone at Boxtree who are always a great encouragement on the Supersoaps projects.

Special thanks are due to Susan Gau of John Gau Productions and all the gang who worked on 31 WEST at BSB – it made 1990 a special year for me; to Michael Furguson of *EastEnders* for taking the time to show me around Albert Square; to Julie Goodyear for making Bet Gilroy the Queen of Soaps and my pin-up; to June Brown who makes Dot Cotton one in a million, thanks for the photo; my mum, Mrs Joyce Stacey, for checking my spelling yet again, and to Simon Cole and John Kavyo of the *Crossroads* fan club. Last but not least, to Ron Eagle and everyone at Tyne Tees and Brian Ellson and the gang at TVMM.

Now sit back, sharpen your pencils and your wits, and enjoy Super Soaps Quiz Book No 3.

Chris Stacey
September 1991

For Fluff, the sunshine and fun in my life

The Great British Soaps

Coronation Street

Coronation Street is now over 30 years old and still going strong. The Street has now become a must on Mondays, Wednesdays and Fridays. Bet Gilroy is still the Queen of the Rovers Return, Alf is still selling his balm cakes, and we all hope they will still be there in another 30 years. There is a special first episode quiz, as over 12 million of us watched the repeat of the first episode in 1990.

A1   What is Alf and Audrey Roberts' address?

A2   What is Gail and Martin's address?

A3   How old was Bet when she was pregnant with Martin Downs?

A4   What was the name of the father of Bet's son and how old was she at the time of the affair?

A5   When was Bet's son born?

A6   How much money did Vera Duckworth get from Baldwins?

A6   Where did Eddie Ramsden take Tina Fowler on their first date?

A8   Name the estate agents who were selling No. 9 for the Roberts?

A9   What was the estate agent's phone number?

A10   For how much did the Roberts sell their house?

A11   Name the department store for which Stephanie Barns worked.

A12   Who did Jenny Bradley take to the Websters' third wedding anniversary party?

A13   What did Rita buy Jenny for her first day at college?

A14   Which polytechnic did Jenny Bradley go to?

A15   Name the man with whom Steph Barns ran off.

Answers on page 77

B1 What was Jackie Ingrams/Baldwin's address?

B2 What was Phil Jenning's car registration number?

B3 For how much did Ken Barlow sell his car?

B4 Who bought Ken's old car?

B5 How many miles had Ken's old car done before he sold it?

B6 What is the phone number of the Rovers Return?

B7 What did Vera Duckworth take from Baldwins as a momento?

B8 Name the students Jenny met on her first day at the polytechnic.

B9 Builder Maurice Jones has a secretary. What is her relationship to him?

B10 When is Ken Barlow's birthday?

B11 Where was Alan Bradley living just before he died?

B12 How much did Maurice Jones charge Alec Gilroy for the Rovers' football strip?

B13 What was the name of the petrol station Mike Baldwin bought in Spain.

B14 How much did Mike pay for the petrol station?

B15 Name the false company Mike set up to buy Jim's Café.

Answers on page 77

C1 When Alma went to view Jackie Ingram's house, what name did she use?

C2 What was the name of Phil Jennings' company?

C3 Which member of the Betterbuys staff was Reg Holdsworth having an affair with in 1990?

C4 What did Stephanie Barns do to Kevin Webster on the night of the Barns' house-warming party?

C5 When Rita disappeared to Blackpool in 1989, where did she stay and what was her room number?

C6 Who told Bet and Alec that Rita was in Blackpool?

C7 Name the toy company Derek Wilton worked for in 1989?

C8 Which Street resident is left-handed?

C9 Who was the goal-keeper at the 1989 five-a-side football match?

C10 What country did Jenny and Flick Karn visit in the summer of 1990?

C11 What did Ivy Brennan become obsessed with attending in 1990?

C12 What holiday destination did Derek and Mavis buy from Alec Gilroy?

C13 How much did Derek pay for this holiday?

C14 Name the holiday company with which the holiday was booked.

C15 What is Mike Baldwin's middle name?

Answers on page 77

D1 Where did Mike Baldwin buy a luxury flat?
D2 What is Victor Pendelbury's company called?
D3 What sort of company car did Victor give Derek?
D4 What is Liz McDonald's nickname for Jim?
D5 Name Alec Gilroy's first wife.
D6 At what address did Tim and Sandra Alden live?
D7 What was Wendy Crozier's address?
D8 Who won the Betterbuys trolley race in 1991?
D9 What did the winner do with the contents of the trolley race?
D10 Name Victor Pendelbury's wife.
D11 Name the dog Jack gave Vera for Christmas in 1991.
D12 Name the investigator from Betterbuys head office.
D13 Which house was robbed in 1991?
D14 Who is the head teacher at Ken Barlow's school?
D15 What is Phil Jennings' real name?

Answers on page 77

E1 What did Tom Casey give his son Mark on his twenty-first birthday?

E2 Name the older man with which Jenny fell in love.

E3 What was his profession?

E4 After Curly, with whom did Kimberley Taylor fall in love?

E5 What was his profession?

E6 What was the name of the posh family who interviewed Jack and Vera for jobs as housekeeper and chauffeur?

E7 For whom did the Duckworths tell the family they worked?

E8 Who is the woman who has a soft spot for Alf Roberts?

E9 Which committee did they both sit on?

E10 What was the name of the product Jenny and Steph helped launch?

E11 Who was the organiser of the promotion?

E12 What place did Phil Jennings want to develop with Alec's help?

E13 What was the name of the company set up by Alec, Phil and Bet?

E14 What was Deirdre's election colour?

E15 Where did Tracey Barlow go on a school trip in 1991?

Answers on page 78

F1 What is the name of Jim McDonald's mother?

F2 Name the opera act who auditioned in the Rovers' bar.

F3 Name the painter with whom Deirdre had an affair.

F4 Where did Emily Bishop plan on moving in 1991?

F5 What is Jackie Ingrams' middle name?

F6 Name the old mate of Mikes who made an offer to buy Ingrams?

F7 Name the company set up by Alma and Gail to run the café.

F8 Which vegetable did Mavis give Derek to make him more sexy?

F9 Who had a schoolboy crush on Steph Barns?

F10 Name all the candidates in the 1991 Weatherfield elections.

F11 How many votes did Deirdre get in that election?

F12 How many votes did Alf get?

F13 Who had a row while Alf was making his winning speech?

F14 What is Deirdre's middle name?

F15 Who designed the Betterbuys carnival float in 1991?

Answers on page 78

The First Episode

G1 Who was the first person seen on screen in the first episode?

G2 Who was taking over the corner shop at the time?

G3 What had just come out of prison?

G4 How much did Elsie Tanner find missing from her purse?

G5 Where was Ida Barlow working at the time?

G6 Where was Ken Barlow meeting his new girlfriend?

G7 What was David Barlow planning on buying in the first episode?

G8 What did Ken Barlow give Dennis Tanner?

G9 Who took the money out of Elsie Tanner's purse?

G10 What was over Elsie Tanner's fireplace in the first episode?

G11 What did Ena Sharples ask Florrie Lindley on their first meeting?

G12 What made David Barlow late for dinner?

G13 From whom did Ken Barlow seek advice?

G14 Who was Ken meant to have been meeting in town?

G15 Who surprised Ken by turning up at No. 1 Coronation Street?

Answers on page 78

EastEnders

EastEnders is still as gripping as it was in the early days. Dot, Pauline and Arthur are still there. During 1991, *EastEnders* has given some of the strongest storylines of any British soap with Eddie's murder, Nick's drug addiction and Mark coming to terms with being HIV positive.

A1 What was the name of Ian's mobile catering business?

A2 Ian bought the Dagmar site in 1991 and had it refurbished. What did he call the building?

A3 Where did Ian store the industrial fridges which he had bought for his catering business?

A4 At what number Albert Square does the Tavernier family live?

A5 In 1990, Pauline and Arthur Fowler celebrated an important wedding anniversary. What was it?

A6 When Mark Fowler returned to Walford in 1990, in what part of the country had he been living?

A7 What is the name of Sharon Watts' real mother?

A8 When Michelle worked for the local council, what was the name of her boss?

A9 Why did Ian Beale crash his van in 1990?

A10 From where was Pauline Fowler made redundant in 1991?

A11 Who moved into 55 Victoria Road in 1991?

A12 Who were the previous tenants at this address?

A13 The Queen Vic has a public phone. What is its number?

A14 On what day does Dot Cotton wash and change her bed sheets and linen?

A15 Mr Popadopoulos owns the launderette in Bridge Street. What is his christian name?

Answers on page 79

B1 Marge Green confessed she had once been a stage manager for a local drama group. What was the name of the group?

B2 At the Queen Vic talent night in 1989, what did Ethel and Reg do?

B3 What did Frank Butcher do to raise money?

B4 Who won the 1989 Queen Vic talent night?

B5 How much did Ali Osman owe in rent to his landlord Macintyre?

B6 Michelle's former boyfriend, Danny Whitting, was married. What was his wife's name?

B7 What were the names of Danny's children?

B8 How old was Marge Green's mother when she died?

B9 What sort of stall does Big Ron own?

B10 What was Trevor Short's date of birth?

B11 What was the name of the reporter who interviewed Marge Green after she was mugged?

B12 What newspaper did the reporter work for?

B13 What was the name of the policeman in charge of Marge's case?

B14 When the OAPs went away for a week in 1989, what seaside town did they visit?

B15 What competition did Dot Cotton win while the OAPs were away?

Answers on page 79

C1 When was Cindy Beale's baby, Steven, born?

C2 How much did Steven Beale weigh when he was born?

C3 What is Cindy Beale's father's name?

C4 What was the name of the Karim's nephew who was lined up to marry Shireen?

C5 How old was the Karim's nephew at that time?

C6 What was the name of the old man who was interested in the Beale family and everyone in Albert Square?

C7 What does Ricky Butcher attend every Wednesday?

C8 How much did Dot win on the newspaper bingo?

C9 To where did Sam and Ricky run off to be married?

C10 What is the name of Clyde Tavernier's son?

C11 Who was Rachel's first lodger?

C12 What job did Etta Tavernier apply for and get?

C13 Where did Diane Butcher arrange to meet Frank when she was ready to return to Walford?

C14 What incident held up the conversion work on the Dagmar?

C15 What was the name of the workman who was hurt while working on the Dagmar?

Answers on page 79

D1 What did Marge Green's mother keep in a glass jar?

D2 Where was the glass jar kept?

D3 What did Marge offer Dot when she was about to be given the sack from the launderette?

D4 How many signatures did Marge collect to keep Dot at the launderette?

D5 What was the name of Cindy Beale's old school?

D6 What was the name of Marge Green's beloved cat?

D7 Who is the new Luxford and Copley brewery area rep?

D8 What is the address and phone number of the Mitchell brothers' lock-up garage?

D9 What did Ian buy that caused a rift between him, Pete and Kathy?

D10 What is the name of Arthur Fowler's gardening business?

D11 What is Celestine Tavernier's job?

D12 What did Pauline and Arthur buy Michelle as a moving-in present when she moved to Rachel's?

D13 What electrical appliance did Rachel refuse to have in her house?

D14 What is the name of Phil and Grant Michell's lawyer?

D15 What is the name of the barmaid who sometimes helps out in the Queen Vic?

Answers on page 79

E1 What did Jackie Stone sell on his stall?

E2 Who did Ricky take to Vince's Hip Hop night at the community centre?

E3 What did Simon arrange for the Queen Vic on the same night as the Hip Hop night?

E4 What goods did Laurie Bates sell on his market stall?

E5 What did Ian rename the café when he took it over from Ali?

E6 How much did Benny Bloom leave Ethel in his will?

E7 What was the name of Benny's nasty daughter who tried to stop Ethel getting the money he left?

E8 Where did Cindy's parents move to?

E9 Why did they move?

E10 Who accidentally knocked Pauline Fowler down with a car?

E11 What was the name of the group Eddie Royle hired for his first night as landlord?

E12 Who was the lead singer with the group?

E13 Who was the unexpected guest singer with the group?

E14 Where does Pauline Fowler's Auntie Betty live?

E15 What did Diane Butcher paint on the side of the B & B?

Answers on page 80

F1 What is Disa's surname?

F2 At what number Albert Square does Dot Cotton live?

F3 What was the name of Disa's stepfather?

F4 What is the Fowlers' telephone number?

F5 How much did Den's funeral cost?

F6 When did Den die, and when was his funeral?

F7 What was the name of the girl who had a crush on Celestine Tavernier?

F8 Which pub did the Queen Vic play in the 1991 quiz night?

F9 Who was the question master at the quiz night?

F10 Who made up the Queen Vic quiz team?

F11 Who did Disa phone the night Ken kidnapped her baby?

F12 What did Kathy rejoin in 1991?

F13 Who won the 1991 quiz night?

F14 Where did Diane go with her college for a field trip?

F15 What is the name of Pat and Frank's B & B?

Answers on page 80

G1 When Mark Fowler returned home, what room did Pauline give him?

G2 With whom did Kathy Beale have a brief affair in 1991?

G3 For which tourist board did Eibhlin, Eddie's girlfriend work.

G4 Which member of the Tavernier family suffers from sickle cell anaemia.

G5 Where did Ricky and Sam lose their virginity?

G6 Who left a newborn baby on the B & B doorstep at Christmas 1990?

G7 What entertainment did Eddie provide in the Queen Vic for New Year's Eve, 1990?

G8 What present did Ian Beale buy for himself as a New Year's treat?

G9 With whom did Sharon Watts spend Christmas 1990, and where did they spend it?

G10 What was the name of the young boy Pete Beale befriended?

G11 Which two country and western stars did Pauline and Arthur Fowler dress up as on New Year's Eve 1990?

G12 In what part of Spain did Frank and Pat Butcher buy a timeshare apartment?

G13 In what year and where did Frank and Pat first meet?

G14 Who was the party bore at Rachel's party in June 1991? He also tried to get Michelle into bed.

G15 What was the name of the guesthouse where the Mitchells and the Butchers stayed when they went to find Sam and Ricky in Gretna Green?

Answers on page 80

Emmerdale

Emmerdale is like a breath of fresh air in the soap world, but its storylines are as strong as any soap on TV today. All *Emmerdale* fans must miss Amos, and they were all upset by the untimely death of Henry Wilks who had been played by Arthur Pentelow since the first episode.

A1 How many trout were stolen from the fish farm the night Mrs Bates' mother was taken ill?

A2 What is Mrs Bates' mother's name?

A3 Over what did Amos and Henry have a big falling out?

A4 Where did Henry stay after the row with Amos?

A5 Where did Dolly arrange for the two to meet?

A6 When is Kate Sugden's birthday?

A7 Name the perfume Kate Sugden used when she was with David Hughes.

A8 Name the girl traveller Matt befriended.

A9 How much did Alan Turner pay for Mrs Bates' cottage?

A10 Where does Mrs Bates' mother live?

A11 How many acres are there on Emmerdale Farm?

A12 Where was Frank Tate's firm based before he moved the business to Home Farm?

A13 What was the phone number of Tates Haulage at that time?

A14 What is the telephone number of Home Farm?

A15 How many acres are there on Home Farm?

Answers on page 81

B1 Where did Elizabeth Feldman send Elsa to stay when she found out she was pregnant?

B2 To which relation was Elsa sent at the time?

B3 How much did baby Alice win on the premium bonds?

B4 Where did Kate Sugden stay when she first came out of prison?

B5 Where did Joe and Kate first meet when she came out of prison?

B6 Where did Nick Bates book a holiday for Elsa, baby Alice and himself in 1991?

B7 With what country did Frank Tate want to twin towns?

B8 What country did Kim Tate suggest and everyone approve?

B9 With what company did Nick Bates book his 1991 holiday?

B10 Name the Woolpack regular who died in the summer of 1991.

B11 What did this person keep in his front room?

B12 Where did Archie Brooks lodge during 1991?

B13 When Alan Turner suffered a rash in the summer of 1991, what did Seth give him for it?

B14 Which member of the Sugden household is a vegetarian?

B15 What was the name of the guest house into which Henry planned to move when he upset Annie?

Answers on page 81

C1 What did Kate Sugden try to plant on Crossgill land?

C2 Where did Rachel Hughes' first driving lesson take place?

C3 Who was Rachel's first driving instructor?

C4 What is the surname of Jack Sugden's girlfriend, Sarah?

C5 When Jack walked out of Emmerdale in 1990, where did he go to work?

C6 What was the name of this place and where was it?

C7 Who was Jack's nasty boss at the time?

C8 When Alan Turner employed David Hughes, how much did he pay him?

C9 How many hours' work per day did Alan Turner give David Hughes?

C10 Frank Tate claims he doesn't drink although he has been known to have a drop or two. What are the other things Frank claims not to do?

C11 What did David Hughes buy Kate Sugden for Christmas 1989?

C12 Who was up at 4.30am on Christmas Day, 1989?

C13 What did Mark Hughes buy Annie for Christmas 1989 (the Hughes' first Christmas at Emmerdale)?

C14 What is the name of the dog that used to sit in the parlour at Emmerdale?

C15 Name the Norwegian who visited Beckingdale in September 1991.

Answers on page 81

D1 What is the name of Beckingdale's local policeman?

D2 What is the local bobby's nickname?

D3 What was the name of the prison Kate Sugden was sent to?

D4 What is the name of Archie Brooks' mother?

D5 Who helped Archie Brooks sell ice cream?

D6 Who worked at Tates as a receptionist for a while?

D7 When did Nick and Elsa plan to marry but didn't quite make it?

D8 What did Dolly discover about herself on the day Nick and Elsa became engaged?

D9 In whom did Dolly confide about her little problem?

D10 Who ate all Alan Turner's bar bites on Turner's first night in the Woolpack?

D11 Who is the manager of the fish farm?

D12 What was the name of the Fieldmans farm?

D13 Who was the owner of that farm?

D14 What did Frank Tate plan to do with Blackthorn Farm?

D15 What did Seth Armstrong lose when he claimed he couldn't work?

Answers on page 81

E1 Who did Dolly Skilbeck have an affair with in 1991?

E2 What operation did Frank Tate have in 1991?

E3 What was the name of the song that Kathy sang at the 1991 talent night?

E4 Who was the host of the 1991 talent night?

E5 What did Chris do on the talent night that made Kathy nervous?

E6 Where did Kathy and Chris live when they first started to live together?

E7 Who bought Demdyke cottage from Joe Sugden?

E8 Name the woman who conned Eric Pollard out of all the money.

E9 Who did Zöe Tate sleep with to upset Rachel and Archie?

E10 What did Dolly do that shocked Kim Tate?

E11 What jobs does Nick Bates do?

E12 Where did Kathy go to live when she left Chris Tate?

E13 Where did Nick and Elsa move to in 1990?

E14 What job had Sarah been doing before she went to work on the farm?

E15 Who took a photo of Alan Turner the day he took over the Woolpack?

Answers on page 82

F1 What did Amos and Henry put in the taproom to boost business?

F2 What did Alan Turner turn the taproom into when he took over?

F3 What was the name of the brewery who supplied Alan Turner with beer just after he took over?

F4 What did Elizabeth draw up to keep Seth under control?

F5 Who are baby Alice's godparents?

F6 Where did Nick and Elsa plan to marry when they didn't quite make it?

F7 Who delivered baby Alice when she was born?

F8 Where did Joe go after he kissed Kim Tate?

F9 Who did Elsa ask to give her away?

F10 How far is Hotton from Beckingdale?

F11 What did Archie's mother ask him if he was?

F12 Who did Nick ask to be his best man at the wedding?

F13 When the residents want a posh meal where do they go?

F14 What did April give Archie when she came to see him?

F15 Who did Kim Tate meet and tell about Dolly's pregnancy?

Answers on page 82

G1 What did Chris give Kathy after her success at the 1990 talent night?

G2 What job did Kathy take on the Tates' estate?

G3 What was the name of the important businessman who was rude to Kathy at the Tates'?

G4 Who moved in to Alan Turner's cottage in 1991?

G5 What did Alan Turner introduce to help beer sales?

G6 What did Alan Turner do to boost custom?

G7 Who did Alan Turner get to do the voice for his radio ads?

G8 After Robert's birthday party in 1991, where did Jack go after his row with Sarah?

G9 What did Dolly give baby Alice as a christening present?

G10 Where was baby Alice christened?

G11 Who moved in to the Woolpack with Alan Turner?

G12 Who did Kate Sugden knock down and kill by accident in 1990?

G13 What is baby Alice's second name?

G14 What was the name of the vet for whom Zöe Tate worked?

G15 Where did Zöe Tate take a job in 1991?

Answers on page 82

Take the High Road and Families

Take the High Road and *Families* are two of ITV's top-rated daytime soaps, although viewers in Scotland can see *Take the High Road* at peak time. Both soaps are enjoyed by millions and have storylines that are as gripping as their peak-time counterparts.

A1 In *Take The High Road*, who was rushed to hospital on the day of TJ and Carol's wedding?

A2 Name the old man for whom Mrs Mack was housekeeper.

A3 Who was TJ Wilson's best man at his wedding?

A4 What name did TJ and Carol give their unborn baby?

A5 What was the first Inverdarroch's real name?

A6 Name Lady Rose Gifford's Tibetan companion.

A7 What is the name of the gossipy postman in Glendarroch?

A8 In *Families*, name Amanda Thompson's house.

A9 What was the name of Anton Vaughan's wife and what happened to her?

A10 Who did Amanda Thompson leave waiting at the church?

A11 What prompted Diana Stevens to return to England after more than 20 years?

A12 Who killed Mike Thompson?

A13 How did John Thompson die?

A14 What was Nathan Thompson charged with by the police after a party?

A15 Name the pub that Larry and Jane Richards run.

Answers on page 83

Crossroads
The Soap that won't wash away

Crossroads has not been shown since 1988, but there has been such a lot of interest in the saga that there are rumours of a movie about the Crossroads Motel. The *Crossroads* fan club have kept viewers up to date with the stars of the soap as well as continuing the soap.

A1 Name the shop owned by Ted and Tish Hope in the 70s.

A2 Who was the motel's hairdresser in the 70s?

A3 Where did Diane Hunter's son Nicky live?

A4 What was the name of the motel's maid who was a Pat Boone fan?

A5 Who was the Scots chef who disappeared from the motel kitchens?

A6 Where did Jill and Adam honeymoon in 1983?

A7 Which special surprise did Adam arrange for Jill on that honeymoon?

A8 Who was the garage manageress in the early 80s?

A9 What was the name of the Downs Syndrome child she befriended?

A10 What was the name of Valerie Pollard's businessman husband?

A11 When the Hunters left the motel in 1985 where did they go?

A12 Who was Meg's chauffeur at her wedding to Hugh in 1975?

A13 Name the globe-trotting journalist with whom David Hunter had an affair in 1975.

A14 Who made Alison Cotterill pregnant?

A15 Who was the singing barmaid who sang at the 1985 Miss Crossroads contest?

Answers on page 83

Brookside

Brookside has recently expanded to three nights a week as well as introducing new locations. Old favourites have left like Sheila and Billy Corkhill and the Collins family, as well as new and interesting families like the Farnhams and the Dixons.

A1 What was the name of the supermarket that Rod Corkhill worked in undercover for the police?

A2 What name did he use while he was working undercover?

A3 Name the estate agents who were selling Harry Cross' bungalow while Mick and Josie were living in it.

A4 Name the couple who looked over the bungalow while Mick and Josie were there but didn't know anything about it.

A5 What was the phone number of the estate agents selling the bungalow?

A6 To what activity did Keith take Jackie on their first date?

A7 What was the name of the place to which Keith took Jackie?

A8 What is Keith's surname?

A9 What is DD Dixon's real name?

A10 What course did Chrissy Rogers want to attend in the summer of 1991?

A11 Which football club did Geoff Rogers train with and hope to play for?

A12 With which football team did Geoff Rogers get a YTS course?

A13 What sort of car does Barry Grant drive?

A14 What did Josie and Marcia run during the summer of 1991?

A15 Who had a night of passion with Sue Sullivan during the summer of 1991?

Answers on page 84

B1 What was the name of the street where Frank Rogers had his car stolen in 1991?

B2 Name the father of Diane Spence (Rod Corkhill's girlfriend).

B3 Name Mick Johnson's brother.

B4 What is Father O'Farrell's christian name?

B5 What is DD Dixon's maiden name?

B6 How tall is Mick Johnson?

B7 Who was Mick Johnson accused of attacking?

B8 Name the two lawyers who handled Mick Johnson's court case.

B9 What business did Tracey Corkhill run?

B10 What job did Tracey Corkhill take in July 1991?

B11 What nickname did Josie give Max and Patricia Farnham?

B12 Name the soap opera that the residents of the close watch.

B13 How much was the deposit that Terry and Sue needed to buy no 9?

B14 Name the woman who looked after Mick Johnson when he was a child.

B15 Name Max Farnham's two children by his former marriage.

Answers on page 84

C1 What was the name of the schoolgirl who blackmailed Katie Rogers?

C2 What was the name of the schoolgirl that Annabelle Collins befriended?

C3 What was the name of the home in which she lived?

C4 Sammy Rogers has a friend called Ronnie Williams. What is her real name?

C5 Name the two men killed in a car crash which left Owen disabled.

C6 What sort of car were they driving?

C7 What was the name of the hospital that Sammy Rogers was taken to?

C8 What hospital was Owen taken to?

C9 How old was Owen at the time of the accident?

C10 How much did Frank and Chrissy Rogers think they were going to have to pay for their dry rot?

C11 Name Frank's workmate who repaired the dry rot cheap and how much did he charge?

C12 What was the name of the woman Ralph Hardwick married?

C13 What was the name of her late husband?

C14 What brought Ralph's future wife to the close?

C15 Where did Alison Gregory go to work?

Answers on page 84

D1 What did Ron Dixon put up between the Dixons' and the Farnhams' houses?

D2 Who took the "Brookside" wall down?

D3 How did Mick Johnson's daughter Gemma go missing?

D4 What was the name of Gemma Johnson's favourite doll?

D5 Name Max Farnham's snooty ex-wife.

D6 Who was the policeman who sat with the Johnsons while Gemma was missing?

D7 Who gave Ron Dixon's mobile shop a coat of paint?

D8 What is the name of Ron Dixon's mobile shop?

D9 How many wives does Cyril Dixon have?

D10 Why did Ron Dixon object to Jackie's friend Keith?

D11 Where did Billy and Sheila Corkhill go to live?

D12 Who are Ron and DD Dixon's best friends?

D13 What was Mike Dixon's media studies project at school?

D14 Where did the Collins family go to live when they left the close?

D15 What was the name of the 60s pop group in which Frank Rogers played?

Answers on page 84

E1 Who did Billy and Jimmy Corkhill try to get revenge on for killing their brother?

E2 What was built between the Sullivans and the Dixons?

E3 With whom did Sammy Rogers go to live in 1991?

E4 What were the names of Tim Derby's son and daughter?

E5 What was Geoff Roger's last girlfriend's name?

E6 Where did Sammy Rogers meet Owen Daniels in 1991, for the first time in more than a year?

E7 Which pop group did Geoff Rogers win tickets to see?

E8 Who was Sue Sullivan's gossip friend at work?

E9 What did DD Dixon confess to her husband Ron in the summer of 1991?

E10 Where did DD Dixon really meet Maria Benson?

E11 How old was DD at the time she first met Maria Benson?

E12 Who had been supplying Josie Johnson with "knock off" stock in 1991?

E13 Where had window cleaner Sinbad been brought up as a child?

E14 Who was Mick Johnson's only witness at his court appearance in 1991?

E15 To whom did Julia Brogan become engaged during the summer of 1991?

Answers on page 85

F1 Name the property company who built the shops at the back of the close.

F2 Who was the man who worked at the property company (he had a pony tail)?

F3 When did Tim Derby throw Sammy Rogers out?

F4 Name Jimmy Corkhill's daughter.

F5 Jimmy also has a son. What is his name?

F6 What was the name of the policeman who tried to rape Tracey Corkhill?

F7 On who did Mike Dixon try to get revenge for trying to push drugs on his sister Jackie?

F8 Who is the keen swimmer on Brookside Close?

F9 Who gave Max Farnham a job in 1991?

F10 Who interviewed Patricia Farnham for the London job?

F11 What top London hotel did Max and Patricia stay in the night after Patricia's London interview?

F12 What is the name of the lawyer who pestered Sue Sullivan at work?

F13 What school does Leo Johnson go to?

F14 There was an outbreak of what with the children of Brookside Close in the summer of 1991?

F15 Who took over ownership of the Brookside shops?

Answers on page 85

G1 What happened to Katie Rogers during the summer of 1990 that put her in hospital?

G2 What did Sheila Corkhill confess to Terry Sullivan during the summer of 1990?

G3 What did Terry do to Sue's things when he found out he wasn't Daniel's real father?

G4 What did Tracey Corkhill do that upset Barry Grant in 1990?

G5 Who agreed to look after Daniel Sullivan when Terry and Sue got back together?

G6 Which two men rowed over Julia Brogan on New Year's Day 1991?

G7 Where did Josie, Mick and the kids go if they wanted a cheap holiday?

G8 What was Mike Dixon's first band called?

G9 How much did Mike's band receive for their first public performance?

G10 What was the name of the club where Mike's band made their debut?

G11 What was the name of Mike's friend who played in the band?

G12 What was the name of Margaret Clemence's ex-boyfriend?

G13 Where does Margaret Clemence's family live?

G14 What does Patricia Farnham collect as a hobby?

G15 What did Barry Grant do to Mark Potter's new car in May 1991?

Answers on page 85

The American Soaps

Dallas

Dallas has finished its last season and it went out on a high note. There was high drama touched with a sense of humour, but *Dallas* will always be known for JR's women, Sue Ellen's drinking, and all those long-lost relations. Let's hope it won't be too long before ol' JR will be pumping oil again.

A1 What was the phone number of April's flat?

A2 What was Rose McKay's maiden name?

A3 Where had Rose McKay been living before she came to Dallas?

A4 What sort of business had Rose been running?

A5 What unusual gift did Bobby give April just before they became engaged?

A6 Who was Christopher Ewing's first date?

A8 In which town did Miss Ellie and Clayton find Jock's first gusher?

A9 Which Ewing once owned a solar energy corporation?

A10 What is the name of the cab firm the Ewings use?

A11 How many acres is Southfork Ranch?

A12 What did Bobby once want to build on Southfork land?

A13 What was the name of the park Miss Ellie saved from having apartments built on it?

A14 What organ did JR have removed after his famous shooting?

A15 What was the name of Sue Ellen's hairdresser?

Answers on page 86

B1 What did JR tell Sue Ellen to do with the film she made about the Ewings?

B2 Who was JR's trusted police informer?

B3 Name the only woman Cliff Barnes has ever loved?

B4 What did Miss Ellie receive in the post addressed to Jock?

B5 Who was the item from?

B6 Who was the most important gallery owner in Dallas?

B7 What was Afton Cooper's daughter's real name?

B8 Who was Afton Cooper's ex-husband?

B9 In the 1989–90 season who turned up at JR's office wondering what a Sly Lovegrove looked like?

B10 Who were the chief mourners at Tommy McKay's funeral?

B11 Vanessa Beaumont first went to Dallas to collect what?

B12 What did James propose a toast to at his first family meal?

B13 What did James give as evidence that JR was his father?

B14 What other dramatic event happened that night?

B15 What was the name of the oid tanker JR bought cheaply?

Answers on page 86

C1 What did James ask Cally if he should call her?

C2 Where did Bobby and April honeymoon in 1990?

C3 Who did Bobby and April take part of the way with them?

C4 Where did Bobby and April drop off these people?

C5 What did Sue Ellen become in 1990–91?

C6 What relation of Clayton's was in the same mental home as JR?

C7 Where was Sue Ellen living in 1990/91?

C8 On what TV show did Cliff appear when he was on the Gulf spillage committee?

C9 How did Bobby give April her engagement ring?

C10 What phone number did Cliff have to use if he was interested in becoming Mayor of Texas?

C11 Where was Cliff Barnes' first meeting with Stephanie Rogers?

C12 Name the oil company that April set up?

C13 Who did April buy the oilfields from?

C14 Name the town Miss Ellie owns.

C15 Who was James' first *Dallas* date?

Answers on page 86

D1 What was the name of the drilling expert JR wanted to help him in Pride?

D2 What was the name of the person who turned up in his place?

D3 How old was this person?

D4 Name the Pam look-a-like that Bobby saw at the Oil Barons Club?

D5 Who is the doorman at the Oil Barons?

D6 For what company did Jeanne O'Brian work?

D7 Who did Bobby go to see to get more information about Jeanne?

D8 What did Michelle Stevens try to start up with James and April?

D9 Who did JR try to get to sniff out oil in Pride?

D10 Where was his oil company based?

D11 Who was running Callaghan Oil?

D12 Name Blackie Callaghan's 80-year-old girlfriend?

D13 Where did Bobby and Cliff take Jeanne to dinner?

D14 On what prime-time TV show did Stephanie Rogers book Cliff?

D15 Who was the host of the show?

Answers on page 86

E1 What was the name of Stephanie Rogers' company?

E2 With whom did James try to do a business deal (JR got wind of it and put a stop to it).

E3 What was the deal going to be?

E4 Who was Duke's sexy daughter who tried to get James in to bed?

E5 Name the Japanese businessman who, with the help of JR, sent Michelle away.

E6 What did JR get hold of that belonged to Stephanie Rogers?

E7 What was the name of the chat show on which Cally appeared?

E8 What did JR get Jessica to sign at the end of the 1990 season?

E9 What airline did Bobby and April fly to Paris?

E10 What did James get JR to sign and what paper did James give his father?

E11 Where was Cally staying after she split with JR?

E12 Who did Bobby and April meet at Charles de Gaulle airport?

E13 In what hotel were Bobby, April and Sheila Foley staying?

E14 Where was Sheila's husband's company based and what was it called?

E15 Who was the doctor who took JR's case when he was admitted to the mental home?

Answers on page 87

F1 What did the inmates do with JR's contract giving him Jessica's voting rights?

F2 What Dallas regular did Bobby and April meet on their first night in Paris?

F3 What did this person tell them was happening in Paris at the time?

F4 What did Bobby have done to remind him of the honeymoon in Paris?

F5 Name the doctor who took over JR's case.

F6 Name the inmate who was after JR?

F7 Who was the oversexed inmate from the mental home who wanted JR in her bed?

F8 What was the warder's nickname for her?

F9 Who kidnapped April Ewing in Paris?

F10 Who was the leader of the card school James joined in place of JR?

F11 What did James lose at the card game?

F12 What was James' night club called?

F13 Who asked Bobby for a donation to get in to the junior *tour de France*?

F14 What did James do to prove he was not JR's son?

F15 Who did Bobby get to follow the car in which April was held hostage?

Answers on page 87

G1 On what did Dr Wykoff put JR to help him with his treatment?

G2 Who went to see JR and was shocked by his appearance?

G3 What did Sly do to try and get in touch with Cally?

G4 What did JR do as soon as he got back to Ewing Oil?

G5 Name all five inmates of the mental home that JR befriended.

G6 What happened to Jordan Lee while he was in Paris?

G7 Where did James go to work after he left Ewing Oil?

G8 What did Sly keep at home?

G9 What was Sheila Foley's real name?

G10 Where was the real Sheila Foley living?

G11 Where did Bobby have April buried?

G12 What was Lee Ann De La Vegas' maiden name?

G13 What did James announce at JR and Vanessa's engagement party?

G14 Who was Liz Adams' boss?

G15 What was Johnny Dancer's real name?

Answers on page 87

Twin Peaks

Twin Peaks has to be the strangest soap ever seen on TV: Agent Cooper with his cups of coffee and who killer Bob is – will we ever know? One thing is for sure: during 1990/1, I ate a lot of cherry pie and found myself saying, "That's a damn fine cup of coffee".

A1   Where was Dale Cooper born?

A2   What was his parents' address?

A3   When was Laura Palmer's last dated entry in her famous diary?

A4   What was Laura's pony called?

A5   How would Agent Cooper describe a good cup of coffee?

A6   Who found Laura's body?

A7   Name the Twin Peaks police receptionist.

A8   What is the name of the mill?

A9   Name Laura's look-a-like cousin.

A10 What prize had Laura won just before she died?

A11 What is the name of Bobby Briggs' mother?

A12 Name the local hotel.

A13 Who runs the hotel?

A14 Name Dale Cooper's secretary.

A15 By what means does Dale Cooper talk to his secretary?

Answers on page 88

B1 Who was the second victim of Killer Bob?
B2 Name the Hornes' backward son.
B3 What is the christian name of the log lady?
B4 Name the local diner.
B5 Who runs the local diner?
B6 Name Agent Cooper's favourite sweet.
B7 How old was Laura when she died?
B8 What was the name of her therapist?
B9 What was the name of the man who grew orchids who Laura befriended?
B10 What other business does the Horne family run?
B11 Name the sex magazine in which Laura advertised.
B12 What business does Ed Hurley run?
B13 How far is Twin Peaks from the Canadian border?
B14 What is the population of Twin Peaks?
B15 Who was Laura's best friend?

Answers on page 88

Knots Landing

Knots Landing is the only primetime soap still running on American TV. It has been running an amazing 11 years. The residents of Knots Landing have had their ups and downs, but at the end of it they are all friends. We all keep wondering if Val and Gary will get back together and will Karen get through an episode without crying?

A1 Who lives at 16972 Seaview Circle?

A2 On what day were Val Ewing's twins born?

A3 At what address does Val live?

A4 Lilimae has been arrested twice. What were the two charges?

A5 Who claimed Greg Sumner was his half-brother?

A6 Name the women who posed as Peter Holister's mother.

A7 Who always referred to Greg Sumner as "Laddie"?

A8 When Laura worked at a real estate agent, who was her boss?

A9 Name Greg Sumners' first wife.

A10 Who was Peter Holister's sister?

A11 Where did Val marry Ben Gibson?

A12 How old was Val when she first married Gary Ewing?

A13 In the early days, who attended the alcholic meeting with Gary?

A14 Name this fellow alcholic's wife.

A15 Who turned up in *Knots Landing* the night Karen was kidnapped?

Answers on page 88

B1 What did Ann Mattherson tell Mac about Paige?

B2 Who found Peter Hollister's body?

B3 Who buried Peter's body to cover up the murder?

B4 Who gave Olivia Cunningham a letter in case anything happened to them?

B5 To whom did Olivia mail this letter?

B6 How much did Laura and Greg's baby weigh when it was born?

B7 What name did Laura give her baby?

B8 Who was to open the children's playground at Lotus Point?

B9 Where does Ann Mattherson live?

B10 In what do workers travel around Lotus Point?

B11 What did Bobby and Betsy call Lilimae?

B12 What is Gary Ewing's address?

B13 Where did Ben Gibson tell Val he was going to work?

B14 What is Karen's secretary's name?

B15 What did Mac and Karen do for Eric when he became a college freshman?

Answers on page 88

C1 Name Cathy Geary's first husband.

C2 What job did Abby and Ben give Joshua Rush?

C3 On what channel was Joshua's TV show?

C4 Who was Gary's trusted engineer at the Empire Valley site?

C5 For what was the Empire Valley site being used?

C6 What had been buried on the Empire Valley site?

C7 What did Gary Ewing give Betsy and Bobby Ewing on their birthday in 1986?

C8 What did Gary Ewing do to the Empire Valley site?

C9 Name the TV evangelist that Joshua Rush replaced.

C10 Name the three charities for which Joshua raised money.

C11 What was the name of Cathy Geary Rush's TV show.

C12 Who almost died from arsenic poisoning in 1986?

C13 When was Michael Fairgate born?

C14 Name the doctor who treated Michael with his teenage problem?

C15 What was Laura Sumner's maiden name?

Answers on page 89

D1 When and where was Laura Sumner born?

D2 To what did Greg Sumner help Peter Hollister become elected.

D3 Name Paul Galverson's right-hand man.

D4 When did Karen and Sid Fairgate first move in to Seaview Circle?

D5 How many bedrooms are there in the McKenzie house?

D6 When were Val and Gary's twins born?

D7 In what hospital were the twins born?

D8 When were the twins reunited with Val?

D9 Who was Abby Ewing's first love?

D10 What was the name of Paige's old boyfriend who turned up at Knots Landing?

D11 Who moved into Laura's old house?

D12 What is the name of their daughter?

D13 Name the girl that Eric Fairgate married.

D14 What was the name of Charles Scott's wife?

D15 Who did Greg Sumner ask to look after Meg just after Laura's death?

Answers on page 89

E1 What did Paige fake to fool her parents and grandparents?

E2 What nationality is Johnny Rourke?

E3 Where did Johnny first stay when he arrived in Knots Landing?

E4 To what hospital did Mac take Meg when she was taken ill?

E5 Who returned to the Landing for Laura's funeral?

E6 Name Greg Sumner's trusted manservant.

E7 Which residents ended up in bed together the night Laura died?

E8 Where was the clinic to which Laura went to die?

E9 Of what did Laura Sumner die?

E10 Who is Meg Sumner's godfather?

E11 What business did Richard Avery have on his return to the Landing?

E12 How did Jason Avery react to his mother's death?

E13 What did Greg Sumner keep on his coffee table?

E14 Why did he keep this object on the coffee table?

E15 What bottled beer does Mac McKenzie like?

Answers on page 89

F1 Who took a shine to Lilimae?
F2 Where did Al Baker live?
F3 What was Al Baker's job?
F4 Who wasn't invited to Betsy and Bobby's third birthday but gate-crashed the party?
F5 What was Lilimae shocked to find out at that party?
F6 Who did Michael Fairgate save from drowning?
F7 How did Abby and Charles first meet in the 1950s?
F8 In what part of America did they meet?
F9 Where did Eric and Linda meet?
F10 Where did Al Baker take Lilimae dancing?
F11 Who was the first man to whom Abby Ewing made love?
F12 What was Judith Scott's maiden name?
F13 How many years had passed since Abby and Charles had last seen each other?
F14 What does Linda Fairgate call Karen?
F15 Where did Karen plan a wedding reception for Linda and Eric?

Answers on page 89

G1 Name Mac's secretary.

G2 What did Al Baker buy to try and convince Lilimae to marry him?

G3 What did Lilimae agree to do?

G4 What is Abby Ewing's favourite drink?

G5 What did Lilimae buy for Al Baker?

G6 How are Olivia and Michael related?

G7 What did Charles Scott ask Abby Ewing to do?

G8 What colour did Greg Sumner paint his rooms after Laura died?

G9 What did both Val and Jill plan for Gary's birthday?

G10 What did the twins make for Gary's birthday?

G11 What do the twins call Gary?

G12 What did Jill Bennett do with Peter Hollister's ashes?

G13 Name Meg Sumner's nanny.

G14 What musical instrument does Johnny Rourke play?

G15 How much did Johnny find in the dealer's log cabin at Lotus Point?

Answers on page 90

Dynasty and The Colbys

Dynasty and *The Colbys* were two of the most glamorous soaps of the 1980s. When *Dynasty* finished, TV executives listened to viewers and a four-hour mini-series was made to tie up all those loose ends.

A1 What was the registration number of the Colby Enterprises helicopter?

A2 Who tried to ruin Krystle's position at Denver Carrington as Head of Public Relations?

A3 Who had Caress kidnapped in *Dynasty*?

A4 What was Jason Colby's gift to his son Miles?

A5 In the first series of *The Colbys*, Connie had a cowboy boyfriend. What was his real name?

A6 Name Steven Carrington's gay lawyer friend.

A7 In the early days of *Dynasty*, Blake had a trusted lawyer. What was his name?

A8 What was Francesca Colby's nickname?

A9 Who was Sammy Jo's real mother in *Dynasty*?

A10 Who from childhood was Prince Michael meant to have married?

A11 On what date was Adam Carrington kidnapped as a baby?

A12 Where did Adam and Claudia Carrington get married?

A13 What is the subsidiary company of Colby Enterprises once owned by Jason Colby's grandfather?

A14 Who double-crossed Blake in the South China Sea oil lease deal?

A15 What did Krystle sell to raise $40,000 to help Matthew Blaisdel's family business?

Answers on page 90

Falcon Crest

Falcon Crest ended its run in America in 1990, but since 1989 viewers with Sky TV have been able to catch up on old episodes. *Falcon Crest* has always been the Queen of soaps. You will need your hankies for the last episode, so be warned.

A1 Who was Richard Channing's partner and co-owner of the race-track?

A2 Name the house Greg Readon co-owns.

A3 Name Richard's two wives before Maggie.

A4 What job did Angela Channing offer Maggie Gioberti on a short-term contract?

A5 Who did Pamela Lynch blackmail?

A6 Who was visiting Richard Channing the night his house was blown up?

A7 What happened to Maggie after the explosion?

A8 With whom was Chase having an affair at the time of the explosion?

A9 What was the name of the wine Wilder Advertising wanted to advertise for Falcon Crest?

A10 What were the names of Cassandra Wilder's mother and brother?

A11 What did Anna Rossinin want to do with Falcon Crest?

A12 Name the ex-Nazi who kidnapped Julia.

A13 What was the life-saving operation Michael Ranson performed on Maggie?

A14 What was the name of Richard Channing's step-father?

A15 What was the name of the church in which Father Christopher worked?

Answers on page 90

The Australian Suds

Neighbours

Neighbours is still as enjoyable as it always was. Long gone are Charlene, Scott and Henry – and didn't we cry when Henry left. We all missed Mrs Mangel at first, but now we all love to hate Dorothy. Madge and Harold are still there along with Jim and Helen.

A1 What was the name of Mrs Mangel's garden gnome?

A2 After whom was the gnome named?

A3 What was John Worthington's profession before he retired?

A4 What was John's deceased wife's name?

A5 What was Gail Robinson's real father's name?

A6 What was Gail's real mother's name?

A7 What are Harold Bishop's three favourite films?

A8 What was the name of the band formed by the Ramsay Street regulars for the 50s night?

A9 What was Charlene's nickname for Scott?

A10 Name Lucy Robinson's boyfriend who was staying in Elliot Park during the school holidays.

A11 Who took Lucy to Emma's party during the same holidays?

A12 What did Dan Ramsay tell Henry he might find at the bottom of the garden?

A13 Who was stealing food from Lassiter's hotel kitchens?

A14 What did he try to do to Mrs Mangel?

A15 What is the name of the scout troop that Harold Bishop runs?

Answers on page 91

B1 What was the name of the estate agent who sold No. 30 both times?

B2 What was the original auction date for No. 30?

B3 What is Jim Robinson's car registration?

B4 Name the journalist who tried to blackmail Paul Robinson.

B5 Of what did Nick Page's grandmother die?

B6 What did Nick do the night Beverley returned from New Zealand (with a new face)?

B7 Who was Des Clarke's boss at the bank?

B8 Name the assistant at the bank with whom Des fell in love.

B9 What was the name of the rival company who wanted to buy the Daniels Corporation?

B10 When was No. 30 finally auctioned?

B11 Who was bidding on No. 30 for Edith Cubb?

B12 What was Edith Cubb's price limit?

B13 How much did Sharon bid before Des could stop her?

B14 What did Jamie Clark swallow which almost killed him?

B15 How much did Nick Page's paintings sell for in the Coffee Shop?

Answers on page 91

C1 What is the name of Paul Robinson's company lawyer?

C2 What is the name of the lawyer who handles the Uduwghwa account?

C3 What did Katie Landers name Bronwyn's cat?

C4 What did Paul decide to have done for Gail's birthday?

C5 Who started a fight with Todd and Nick at the school disco over Sharon?

C6 What did Nick receive from this fight?

C7 Who was the DJ at the disco?

C8 What is the name of John Worthington's daughter?

C9 Hoping that she should win the cake competition, what did Sharon put in Mrs Mangel's cake?

C10 What happened to Madge's cake?

C11 Who was the judge of the cake competition?

C12 Who won the cake competition?

C13 How much did Joe Mangel charge Des to refit the Coffee Shop?

C14 Who did Mike Young stand in for at Erinsborough High after he left teacher training college?

C15 Who made a pass at Gemma Ramsay the night of Ryan's party?

Answers on page 91

D1 How many points did Todd score on the video game to reach second place?

D2 Who was at the number one spot and how many points did he have?

D3 How many points did Todd score to get to number one on the video games?

D4 Who was second, third and fourth on the video game when Todd was number one?

D5 What did Mrs Mangel get just before her wedding?

D6 Who was John Worthington's best man when he married Nell Mangel?

D7 Where did John's daughter live (it was the same place where John and Nell planned to honeymoon)?

D8 What is Harold Bishop's car registration number.

D9 Name Madge's sexy old schoolfriend who turned up to see her.

D10 How many times had she been married?

D11 In what competition did Madge and Helen enter the Bishops and the Robinsons?

D12 What was the name of the magazine who ran the competition?

D13 What was the name of the cosmetic company for whom Jane Harries worked?

D14 What perfume does Madge wear when she wants a sexy night in with Harold?

D15 Name Melissa Jarret's parents and brother.

Answers on page 91

E1 What names did Gail Robinson give her triplets?

E2 Name the radio station for whom Henry Ramsay worked.

E3 Which two neighbours like pineapple doughnuts?

E4 What job did Bronwyn get just before she left Ramsay Street?

E5 What did Bronwyn call the possum that she looked after?

E6 What is the rival hotel complex called?

E7 Who is the boss of the complex?

E8 Give the surnames of the candidates for the 1990 Erinsborough elections.

E9 Who took over the "Dear Georgette" column in the local newspaper for a while?

E10 Where did Pete Baxter go to train for the Olympics?

E11 For what was Pete training?

E12 Who went along with Pete Baxter to watch him train?

E13 How much ice cream did Des over-order by accident?

E14 What did Henry suggest Des do to get rid of the ice cream?

E15 Name the student Mike Young was caught kissing.

Answers on page 92

F1 Name the old boyfriend of Beverley's who came back in to her life in 1990.

F2 What false name was Caroline Alessi using when she first came to Ramsay Street?

F3 What was the name of the mad author for whom Scott Robinson worked?

F4 Name the girl Mike Young met at the Australian Institute of Sport.

F5 What were Beverley and Ewan researching as doctors?

F6 What did Paul buy from Rosemary Daniels?

F7 What sort of business does Josh Anderson's father run?

F8 Name the English lord that Madge and Harold met while on a trip to England.

F9 How much did Madge Bishop win on the National Lottery?

F10 How much did Madge and Harold give to each of their children?

F11 What language did Des try to learn unsuccessfully?

F12 What was the name of Mike Young's paraplegic girlfriend?

F13 Why was Mike so protective towards her?

F14 Where did Nick Page to to study art?

F15 What did Nick give everyone just before he left?

Answers on page 92

G1 How did Rob Lewis die?

G2 Where did Gail Robinson go to live when she left Paul?

G3 What was Todd's biker friend Boof's real name?

G4 What did Todd buy against Beverley and Jim's wishes?

G5 What did Boof make Todd do that got him into trouble with the police?

G6 What was the name of the patient who kept pestering Beverley?

G7 Helen found a long-lost painting when she bought some frames. What was the name of this famous Australian artist?

G8 Helen traced the owner of the painting and fell in love with him. What was his name?

G9 Where did Henry go to work?

G10 What was the surname Matt was using when he first came to Ramsay Street?

G11 Who is Matt's real mother?

G12 What was the name of the old lady that Kerry, Joe and Toby befriended?

G13 Where did Kerry and Joe get married?

G14 Where did Bronwyn and Henry marry?

G15 What was the name of the woman Harold met while he was jogging (she almost broke up his marriage to Madge)?

Answers on page 92

Home and Away

Home and Away keeps us watching with its interesting stories. Poor Bobby has had a lot of problems and Grant Mitchell has shown up in Summer Bay. Millions tune in each week day to enjoy a bit of Australian sunshine.

A1 What was the name of the Fletcher's dog that was poisoned in the early days?

A2 What is the name of the dog the Fletcher family currently own?

A3 What was Frank Morgan's first job in Summer Bay?

A4 Of which city is Summer Bay just north?

A5 Why did Lance and Martin hate Mr Fisher so much?

A6 In the first episode who protected Bobby from Lance and Martin?

A7 What was the name of the pop group that Frank formed?

A8 Who was the lead singer of this band before Pippa took over?

A9 Why didn't Pippa want to be the lead singer at first?

A10 Who was the first compere of the *Home and Away* variety night?

A11 Who almost drowned in the early days?

A12 What did Floss have a talent for reading?

A13 Who sings the theme song to *Home and Away*?

A14 When were Steven's parents killed?

A15 Where was Steven the night his parents were killed?

Answers on page 93

B1 Name the two men Bobby met through a computer dating agency.

B2 What is the name of the Diner where everyone meets?

B3 Who are joint owners of the Diner?

B4 What is the name of the local paper?

B5 What did Bobby win in her final year of school?

B6 Who was the most popular student at the school in 1988?

B7 What is the name of the school of which Donald Fisher is head teacher?

D8 Name Ruth Stewart's baby.

B9 What is the name of Matt Wilson's rich and nasty uncle?

B10 What did Carly try to sell door-to-door?

B11 Who was the rep. from the door-to-door sales firm?

B12 For how much did Carly buy her door-to-door stock?

B13 What was Morag Bellingham's nickname in her youth?

B14 Who are Bobby's real parents?

B15 What is the name of Carly's twin sister?

Answers on page 93

C1 What was the name of the pop group that Lance, Martin and Marilyn sang in (badly)?
C2 Name the Australian TV pop presenter and quiz show host who appeared in *Home and Away* as a pop presenter.
C3 Name the hit song that Lance and Martin wrote.
C4 To whom did Martin accidently become engaged?
C5 From whom did Tom and Pippa buy the caravan park?
C6 How are Alf and Fisher related?
C7 What did Marilyn leave Summer Bay for a while to become?
C8 Who is Adam and Marilyn's former landlord?
C9 What are the names of Emma Jackson's brothers?
C10 What is Mullet's real name?
C11 Name Mullet's mother.
C12 What did Paul Jenson's father do for a living?
C13 What did Sally and Mullet sing at the 1990 Amateur night?
C14 Why is Mullet so called?
C15 Name Bobby's adopted father.

Answers on page 93

D1 What was the name of Morag Bellingham's dog?

D2 For what company did Nicholas Walsh work?

D3 What animals did Ben buy to try and save money?

D4 Of what did Sally's grandmother die?

D5 What is Marilyn's surname?

D6 Where had Ben Lucini been working before he settled in Summer Bay?

D7 What sort of vehicle did Ben drive during that time?

D8 What did Lance and Martin join?

D9 Name the man who Marilyn dated to make Matt jealous.

D10 Where did this man work?

D11 What was the name of Carly's grandmother?

D12 What did she leave Carly in her will?

D13 How much had this item been valued for?

D14 Name the lawyer and law firm who came to see Carly about her grandmother's will.

D15 Who did Al Simpson beat up and hide in the caravan?

Answers on page 93

E1 Who was going out on a romantic evening the night of Tom's accident?

E2 Who offered to give Sally and Mullet dancing lessons?

E4 Who was travelling in the car with Tom at the time of his accident?

E5 Where had Tom and the other passengers been?

E6 Who was first on the scene of the accident?

E7 What did Steven do to try and save Tom?

E8 Who phoned for the ambulance?

E9 Where did the accident happen?

E10 Who told Pippa that Tom was dead?

E11 How did Pippa react?

E12 Where was Frank Morgan working at the time of Tom's accident?

E13 What had Tom suffered from shortly before the accident?

E14 Who demanded Steven see a doctor after the accident?

E15 Who was visiting Alf and Ailsa at the time of Tom's accident?

Answers on page 94

F1 Name the nasty foster child who stayed with the Fletchers.

F2 How did Dr Philip Matherson die?

F3 Who was responsible for Celia's shop fire?

F4 Who did an impersonation of Elvis at the Amateur night?

F5 What was the main reason Grant Mitchell organised the Amateur night?

F6 Who ran off stage due to nerves?

F7 Who performed a magic act?

F8 Who claimed Grant Mitchell tried to rape her?

F9 What happened when Pippa and Ben first met?

F10 What is the telephone number of Alf Stewart's store?

F11 Who wrote a love letter to Steven?

F12 Who did Steven think was sending him love letters?

F13 Who had a fight with Steven over the love notes?

F14 With whom did Geoff Lime have a romantic birthday picnic?

F15 What is the name of Jennifer Atkinson's husband?

Answers on page 94

G1 How is Jennifer Atkinson related to Alf Stewart?

G2 What was Jennifer's husband's job?

G3 What is the name of Geoff Lime's mother?

G4 What did Geoff's mother accuse Bobby of wanting from Geoff?

G5 Name the deputy head who had a drink problem.

G6 What are Karen and Blake Dean's favourite films?

G7 How did Carly lose her brooch?

G8 With whom has Adam got his biggest cleaning contract?

G9 What is Matt Wilson's main job?

G10 Who were Bobby's guests at the dinner party to introduce Geoff to everyone?

G11 What were Chris Reynold's wife and daughter's names?

G12 What did Viv and Tammy's father do to them when he thought they had misbehaved?

G13 What was the name of the old friend of Carly's who had married a rich man and was showing off?

G14 Who was Viv and Tammy's social worker?

G15 What did Celia Stewart give Ben and Carly as a wedding present?

Answers on page 94

Prisoner Cell Block H

Prisoner Cell Block H has suffered from regional scheduling which means viewers in different ITV regions see different episodes. In December 1991, Central TV ran out of episodes, but the girls from the *Prisoner* fan club will not give up that easily. Who knows, there could be a re-run of the whole series!

A1 What position was Colleen Powell offered when Vera Bennett left Wentworth?

A2 What position had Colleen Powell held?

A3 What job did Vera Bennett take when she left Wentworth?

A4 What present did Heather (Mouse) Trapp give Vera on the day she left the prison?

A5 What was the name of Bea Smith's late husband?

A6 Of what did Bea's mother die?

A7 What was the name of Jim Fletcher's wife?

A8 What was the name of the prison social worker who took over when Paul Reed left?

A9 What was the name of Meg Morris' first husband?

A10 Who killed Meg's first husband?

A11 What was the name of Sid Humphry's nasty son?

A12 Name the ex-crim. who helps run the prison reform group.

A13 Who is head of the Department of Corrective Services?

A14 What is the name of the Wentworth receptionist?

A15 Name Doreen Burns' pen-pal.

Answers on page 95

B1 What is Joan Ferguson's nickname?

B2 What was the name of the prisoner who was allowed to work at reception?

B3 What was the name of the prisoner who had artistic talent?

B4 Name Doreen Burnes' ex-husband.

B5 What was Erica Davidson's maiden name?

B6 Name Lizzie Birdsworth's late husband.

B7 Who killed Judy Bryant's girlfriend, Sharon Gilmore?

B8 What did Judy do to try and get revenge on Sharon's killer?

B9 Meg Jackson had a neighbour who beat her children. What was her name?

B10 Judy Bryant did what on the outside as a job?

B11 Who got stuck in the Wentworth air-conditioning system while trying to escape?

B12 What is the name of the nearest prison to Wentworth?

B13 Name the Wentworth kitchen supervisor.

B14 Which officer proposed to Vera Bennett but was killed?

B15 Kathy Hall was once married to one of Wentworth's prison officers. What was his name?

Answers on page 95

The Flying Doctors

The Flying Doctors shows us life in the Australian outback. Chris, Geoff and Kate along with Sam, Emma and DJ go from one drama to another in the Nimrod aircraft. Every episode is full of high tension and the fun which keeps us watching.

A1 What were the names of the two street boys that George Baxter adopted for a week?

A2 What is the name of Maggie Hutton's brother?

A3 What was the name of the nursing sister who took over when Kate Welling went on holiday?

A4 What job does Paula Patterson do at the Royal Flying Doctor Service?

A5 What is the name of Maggie Hutton's son, who disowned his mother?

A6 Who caused George Baxter to have an accident by parking a van on George's airstrip as he was trying to land?

A7 What is Sam and Emma Patterson's shortwave radio call sign?

A8 What is the shortwave radio call sign of the Flying Doctors plane that Sam flies?

A9 What is the shortwave radio call sign of the Flying Doctors base?

A10 Who runs and operates the Coopers Crossing telephone switchboard?

A11 What is the nearest town to Coopers Crossing?

A12 What was the name of the religious preacher whose road show visited Coopers Crossing?

A13 Who was the young reborn country and western singer who toured with him?

A14 Who is the friendly Aborigine who pops up now and then?

A15 Into what book did Marty Jarvis try to get?

Answers on page 95

The Satellite Soaps

Satellite TV is going from strength to strength. Sky TV shows some of the best American daytime soaps: *The Bold and The Beautiful* and *The Young and the Restless* are two of the top-rated soaps and Lifestyle shows one of the world's longest running soaps, *Search for Tomorrow*.

The Satellite Soaps

A1 In Lifestyle's *Search for Tomorrow*, what is the name of the town in which the characters live?

A2 In Sky One's fashion soap *The Bold and the Beautiful*, what is the name of the fashion house?

A3 In Sky One's *The Young and the Restless*, what is the name of Kay Chancellor's late husband whose grave is at the bottom of her garden?

A4 What is the name of the cosmetic company run by the Abbot Family in *The Young and the Restless*?

A5 In *The Young and the Restless*, what is the name of Kay Chancellor's maid?

A6 The *Young and the Restless* high flyer Victor Newman has a tower-block named after him. What is it called?

A7 How many children do *The Bold and the Beautiful's* Eric and Stephanie Forester have?

A8 In which town do the young and the restless live?

A9 What was the name of Jill Abbot's boyfriend and laywer in *The Young and the Restless*.

A10 In Sky One's *Santa Barbara*, who was the Coronation killer?

A11 Who did *Santa Barbara's* CC Capwell nearly marry (but he stopped the wedding when he found his bride had a dark secret)?

A12 In Sky One's *Young Doctors*, who is the grumpy nursing sister?

A13 Where do the residents of Sky One's *Another World* live?

A14 Who is the Queen of *Search for Tomorrow*?

A15 Who was *Santa Barbara's* Amy Perkins having an affair with while she was pregnant?

Answers on page 96

For Soap Experts Only

Are you a soap expert? The British love soaps and they are top of the TV ratings. But how much do you really know about the world of soaps? If you answer all these questions, consider yourself well on the way to becoming a soap expert. Good luck.

A1 In *Crossroads*, whose catchphrase was "me lips are sealed"?

A2 Who lived at No. 5 Coronation Street between 1961 and 1975?

A3 Who spoke the very first words in the very first episode of *Dallas*, and what were they?

A4 How much would Arthur Fowler from *EastEnders* charge you to do your garden?

A5 What was *Brookside's* original title?

A6 In *Falcon Crest*, what does Richard Channing drink?

A7 Who wrote the original theme to *Dynasty* and *The Colbys*?

A8 In *Prisoner Cell Block H*, what is Erica Davidson's nickname?

A9 What is the name of the stables in *Trainer*?

A10 In *Howard's Way*, what was Jan Howard's fashion house called?

A11 What was the name of the British Satellite Broadcasting (BSB) soap set in deep space?

A12 Name the township where *The Flying Doctors* is filmed.

A13 In *Home and Away*, what businesses did Alf Stewart own by the time he was 30?

A14 On what date was *EastEnders* first shown in the UK and how many people watched?

Answers on page 96

Answers

The Great British Soaps

Coronation Street

A1 5, Grasmere Drive, Weatherfield GM1 4HM.

A2 33 Hammond Road, Weatherfield GN1 4GH.

A3 16 years old.

A4 Joe Mason and he was 28 years old.

A5 13th October, 1956.

A6 £1,947.

A7 The Pizza Hut, Weatherfield.

A8 Simpson and Simpson.

A9 715 53473.

A10 £25,000.

A11 Harrisons Department Store.

A12 Stuart Hanley.

A13 A filofax.

A14 Manchester Poly.

A15 Simon Beaty.

B1 17 Elmgate Gardens, Weatherfield.

B2 PJ1.

B3 £1,450.

B4 Curly Watts.

B5 52,000 miles.

B6 715 2251.

B7 The time clock that they use to clock in and out.

B8 Kate Wilburton and Stuart Haley.

B9 His mother-in-law.

B10 9th October.

B11 31 Radford Street, the other side of the red rec.

B12 £80.

B13 Alcazar.

B14 £150,000.

B15 Alcazar Holdings.

C1 Mrs Halliwell.

C2 PJ Leisure.

C3 Rene Dodds.

C4 Stephanie shaved off Kevin's moustache.

C5 The Strand Hotel, Room No. 14.

C6 Cyril Partridge.

C7 Chuckles Unlimited.

C8 Ken Barlow.

C9 Curly Watts.

C10 France.

C11 The spiritualist meetings at the spiritualist church.

C12 Madeira.

C13 Sunrise Tours.

C14 Vernon.

D1 Weatherfield Docks.

D2 Pendelbury Paper Products or PPP.

D3 A converted ambulance.

D4 Mac.

D5 Joyce.

D6 Chestnut Drive.

D7 47 Church Road, Weatherfield.

D8 Rita Fairclough.

D9 Rita donated the goods to Weatherfield General Hospital.

D10 Yvonne.

D11 Boomer.

D12 Brendan Scott.

D13 The Wiltons at No. 4.

D14 Mrs Jeffers.

D15 Philip Smith.

E1 The Garage where Mark was the trainee.

E2 Robert Weston.

E3 He was a dentist.

E4 Adrian Gosthorpe.

E5 He was mortgage manager at Weatherfield Building Society.

E6 The Maxwell Glovers of Cheshire.

E7 Sir Alec and Lady Gilroy Holdsworth.

E8 Vivien Barford.

E9 W.A.R.T. – the Weatherfield Association of Retail Traders.

E10 Pom De Lite.

E11 Clive Parnell.

E12 The Graffiti Club.

E13 Alphabet.

E14 Yellow.

E15 Tracey went to France.

F1 Maisie.

F2 Tudor Parry Jones.

F3 Dave Barton.

F4 Rhos-on-Sea.

F5 Rachel.

F6 Charlie Travers.

F7 Rosamund Caterers.

F8 Parsnips.

F9 Steve McDonald.

F10 Edward Andrews, Susan Badel, Deidre Barlow, Sylvia Jessup, Thomas Kernan, Alf Roberts.

F11 904 votes.

F12 1,515 votes.

F13 Audrey Roberts and Vivienne Barford.

F14 Ann.

F15 Angie Freeman.

G1 Elsie Lappin.

G2 Florrie Lindley.

G3 Dennis Tanner.

G4 2 shillings or 10p.

G5 The kitchens of the Imperial Hotel.

G6 The Imperial Hotel.

G7 A motor bike.

G8 10 cigarettes.

G9 Linda Cheviskie, Elsie's daughter.

G10 A set of flying ducks.

G11 Her place of worship.

G12 The tyre on David's bike had burst.

G13 Albert Tatlock.

G14 Susan Cunningham.

G15 Susan Cunningham.

Eastenders

A1 Beales On Wheels.

A2 The Meal Machine.

A3 Ian stored the fridges in Pete Beale's flat in Walford Towers.

A4 No. 27 Albert Square.

A5 Their 25th, a Silver Wedding Anniversary.

A6 Newcastle.

A7 Carol Hanley.

A8 Stuart Kendle.

A9 Cindy, his wife, told him he was not the father of her son, Steven.

A10 Tates, the paint factory.

A11 Rachel Kominsky.

A12 The Karim family.

A13 The telephone number is 081–503–7731.

A14 Wednesday regular as clockwork.

A15 Demitrius.

B1 The Walford Players.

B2 They danced the bolero.

B3 Frank stripped to his boxer shorts.

B4 Julie Cooper, the hairdresser.

B5 £900.

B6 Mandy.

B7 Lauren, Wayne and Nichola.

B8 93.

B9 Ron runs a hardware stall.

B10 16th October 1968.

B11 Jenny Masterson.

B12 *The Walford Gazette*.

B13 Det. Sgt. Hopkins.

B14 Clacton-on-Sea, Essex.

B15 The Cha Cha Cha Competition.

C1 28th December 1989.

C2 Four and a half pounds.

C3 Edwin Williams.

C4 Khalil.

C5 19.

C6 Harry.

C7 He attends the college on a mechanics course.

C8 £10,000.

C9 Gretna Green.

C10 Kofi.

C11 Karen, Clyde's girlfriend.

C12 Head teacher.

C13 Kings Cross Station (BR).

C14 One of the workmen hit a live electric cable.

C15 Denny Vickers.

D1 5p coins.

D2 Under the floorboards.

D3 £149.25p, all in 5p coins.

D4 1,553 signatures.

D5 Holy Rood RC Primary School and Church.

D6 Tibby.

D7 Lesley Fisher, a woman rep.

D8 The Arch Garage, Walford, E20, Tel: 081–503–3217.

D9 The Dagmar site.

D10 Fowler and Son.

D11 Claims officer at DHSS.

D12 A television set.

D13 A television set.

D14 Marcus Christie.

D15 Tracey.

ANSWERS

E1 Bric-à-brac.
E2 Marie.
E3 A darts match with a £25 prize.
E4 Cheap fruit and vegetables.
E5 The Bridge Street Café.
E6 £2,000.
E7 Margaret Stone.
E8 Devon.
E9 Because Cindy's father got a job there.
E10 Ricky Butcher in one of Frank's cars.
E11 The Bold Ones.
E12 Karen.
E13 Sharon Watts. She sang "Stormy Weather".
E14 Leigh-on-Sea.
E15 A street art painting of the Square.

F1 O'Brien.
F2 25 Albert Square, Walford, E20.
F3 Ken Rayner.
F4 081-503-0695.
F5 £1,450, but it was reduced by £140.
F6 Den died on 16th February 1989. The funeral was on 1st May 1990.
F7 Yvonne or Sister Yvonne.
F8 The Rose and Crown.
F9 Eddie Royal.
F10 Phil Mitchell, Arthur Fowler, Ethel Skinner, Ricky Butcher and Willy the dog.
F11 Disa phoned the Samaritans.
F12 The Samaritans.
F13 The Queen Vic, on a tie-breaker question.
F14 Paris.
F15 Abercorn House.

G1 Lou's old room, the front room.
G2 Eddie Royle.
G3 The Irish Tourist Board.
G4 Lloyd Tavernier.
G5 In a hotel room in Ilford.
G6 Disa O'Brien.
G7 A Karaoke night.
G8 A mobile phone.
G9 Sharon spent Christmas in Scotland with Grant Mitchell, fishing.
G10 Jason Warren.
G11 They dressed up as Dolly Parton and Kenny Rogers.
G12 Benamadena.
G13 In 1958 at Butlins, Clacton-on-Sea.
G14 Graham.
G15 The Wee Dug Bed and Breakfast Gretna Green.

Emmerdale

A1 40 trout went missing.
A2 Alice Wood.
A3 Spicey Lincolnshire sausages.
A4 Henry went to live at the Mill with Dolly.
A5 They meet at Hotton Park Bowling Green.
A6 13th October.
A7 Blue Grass.
A8 Teri.
A9 £40,000.
A10 Scarborough.
A11 Around 280 acres.
A12 Canal Road, Beckindale.
A13 0757 390524.
A14 Beckindale 63099.
A15 650 acres.

C1 Mustard seeds.
C2 On a private road leading up to Emmerdale Farm.
C3 Joe Sugden.
C4 Connelly.
C5 Jack was working in a chip shop.
C6 The Chippy, Skipdale.
C7 Sidney Flowers.
C8 £2.50p per hour.
C9 20 hours work per week.
C10 Frank does not hunt, shoot or fish.
C11 A German Shepherd puppy dog.
C12 Robert Sugden.
C13 Strawberry bath salts and lavender talc.
C14 Lucy.
C15 Toril Bokeland.

B1 Knaresborough.
B2 Her Auntie Margaret.
B3 £1,000.
B4 Kate went to Sheffield to stay with her father.
B5 In Leeds city centre.
B6 Rhodes.
B7 France.
B8 Norway.
B9 Hotton Travel.
B10 Bill Whiteley.
B11 Bill kept a coffin in his front room.
B12 Archie had been lodging with Bill Whiteley.
B13 One of his wife Meg's potions.
B14 Rachel Hughes.
B15 Daleview.

D1 Sgt. McArthur.
D2 Mac.
D3 Lower Barson.
D4 April Brookes.
D5 Sam Skilbeck.
D6 Rachel Hughes.
D7 On Valentines Day, 14th February 1991.
D8 Dolly discovered she was pregnant.
D9 Jack Sugden.
D10 Seth Armstrong.
D11 Elizabeth Feldman.
D12 Blackthorn Farm.
D13 Frank Tate.
D14 Frank wanted to turn the farm into a farm museum.
D15 Seth lost his famous knitted hat.

E1 Charlie Anidow.

E2 A vasectomy reversal operation.

E3 "Just this side of love".

E4 Tony Charlton.

E5 Chris hired professional recording equipment to record Kathy's song.

E6 They lived on the Tates Estate in the converted nursery.

E7 Dolly Skilbeck.

E8 Debbie Wilson.

E9 Michael Feldman.

E10 Dolly had an abortion.

E11 Nick has two jobs: a paper round and he is the Tates' gardener.

E12 Kathy went to live with Nick and Elsa.

E13 Demdyke Cottage.

E14 A librarian in a mobile library.

E15 Henry Wilkes.

F1 A jukebox and a fruit machine.

F2 An up-market restaurant.

F3 Skipdale Brewery.

F4 A roster so she could keep an eye on Seth.

F5 Alan Turner and Dolly Skilbeck.

F6 Hotton register office.

F7 Zöe Tate.

F8 France.

F9 Alan Turner.

F10 Six miles from each other.

F11 April asked Archie if he was gay.

F12 Archie Brooks.

F13 The Feathers pub and restaurant.

F14 A building society pass book with £500 in it.

F15 Kim told Charlie Aindow that Dolly was pregnant with his baby.

G1 A framed silver disc of her song.

G2 Kathy is the Tates' stable-hand.

G3 Arthur Bright.

G4 Michael and Elizabeth Feldman.

G5 A Happy Hour.

G6 Pay for radio commercials.

G7 Seth Armstrong.

G8 Jack camped in a field to prove he was still young enough to do it.

G9 A silver tankard.

G10 St Mary's, Beckindale.

G11 Caroline Bates.

G12 Pete Whiteley.

G13 Rose.

G14 Martin Bennet.

G15 New Zealand.

Take the High Road and Families

A1 Mrs Mack.

A2 Mr McPherson.

A3 Kenny Tosh.

A4 Sebastian.

A5 Tom Kerr.

A6 Kalsang.

A7 Fergus Jamieson.

A8 Blaze.

A9 Anton's wife's name was Julie and she died in a car crash.

A10 Neil Brooks.

A11 Her father, George, had a heart attack and she wanted to be with him.

A12 His brother, John Thompson.

A13 He set fire to the garage, (the family business).

A14 A drugs charge.

A15 The Railway Hotel.

Crossroads
The soap that won't wash away

A1 The Hope Chest.

A2 Vera Downend.

A3 In America.

A4 Mrs Tardebigge.

A5 Shughie McFee.

A6 Venice.

A7 For her mother, Meg, to visit.

A8 Sharon Metcalfe.

A9 Nina Paget.

A10 J. Henry Pollard.

A11 They went on a world tour.

A12 Larry Grayson.

A13 Angela Kelly, or Kelly to her friends.

A14 Chris Hunter.

A15 Mandy Jorden.

Brookside

A1 Ainsworths Supermarket.

A2 Mr C. Watts (Curly Watts from *Coronation Street* – it was a joke).

A3 Binenan Estate Agents.

A4 Mr and Mrs Jenkins.

A5 051–259–9106.

A6 Ten-pin bowling.

A7 Hollywood Bowles.

A8 Ronny.

A9 Diane Dixon.

A10 A teachers' course.

A11 Tranmere Rovers.

A12 Torquay United.

A13 A jeep.

A14 Josie ran a market stall.

A15 Barry Grant.

B1 Mulberry Street, Liverpool L7.

B2 Freddie Spence.

B3 Ellis Johnson.

B4 Derek.

B5 Diane O'Farrell.

B6 6ft 2ins.

B7 Kenneth James Brady.

B8 Mr McGinn and Mr Fowler.

B9 A mobile hairdressing business.

B10 A job as a hairdresser on a cruise ship.

B11 Lord and Lady Snooty.

B12 Meadowcroft Park.

B13 £4,000.

B14 Auntie Lou.

B15 Matthew and Emily.

C1 Bagga.

C2 Louise Mitchell.

C3 Chadwick House.

C4 Veronica Williams.

C5 Tony and Kay.

C6 A black Ford Escort XR3i.

C7 Ormskirk Hospital, Lancs.

C8 Walton Hospital, where he was in a coma.

C9 He was aged 18.

C10 £1,200.

C11 Lennie and he charged £500.

C12 Lana Castello, a rich American widow.

C13 Carter Castello.

C14 She met Annabella's mother Mona in Las Vegas and decided to pay Mona a visit.

C15 Harvard College.

D1 A wall of old doors.

D2 Father Derek O'Farrell and Margaret Clemence.

D3 Gemma got out of Mick's cab while Mick went to the toilet.

D4 Caries – she never went anywhere without it.

D5 Susannah Farnham.

D6 P.C. Gray.

D7 Keith Rooney.

D8 The Moby.

D9 Three wives.

D10 Because he was black.

D11 Basingstoke.

D12 Maria and Charlie Benson.

D13 30 years of *Coronation Street*.

D14 Kendell.

D15 The Scotty Dogs.

E1 Joey Godden.
E2 A path to the new shop development.
E3 Tim Derby.
E4 Chloe and Adam.
E5 Paula Henegan.
E6 In a disco.
E7 The Farm.
E8 Fran Pearson.
E9 She had been a novice nun.
E10 DD met Maria in a mental home where she had been recovering from a nervous breakdown.
E11 17 years old.
E12 Jimmy Corkhill.
E13 An orphanage.
E14 Frank Rogers.
E15 Cyril Dixon.

F1 Mondred Developments.
F2 Jed Smith.
F3 Just before her 18th birthday.
F4 Lindsay Corkhill.
F5 James Corkhill, or Jimmy.
F6 Mark Potter.
F7 Sinnot.
F8 Jackie Dixon.
F9 Geoffrey Fletcher.
F10 John Willis.
F11 The Tower Thistle Hotel.
F12 Graham Curtis.
F13 Manor Park Infant School.
F14 A bad case of head lice.
F15 Barry Grant.

G1 Katie fell into a stream of bad water.
G2 Sheila confessed that Bobby Grant was not Barry's father.
G3 He burnt all her clothes.
G4 Tracey had an abortion (she was carrying Barry's baby).
G5 Jack Sullivan.
G6 Cyril Dixon and Jack Sullivan.
G7 Cardiff.
G8 The Brave Intention.
G9 £5 between five of them.
G10 The British Legion.
G11 Carl Crawford.
G12 Kieran.
G13 Oldham.
G14 Tea pots.
G15 Barry scratched Mark's car with a coin.

The American Soaps

Dallas

A1 The Dallas Area code and then 555–6885.
A2 Daniels.
A3 Follet.
A4 A hair and beauty parlour.
A5 A musical pendant.
A6 Whitney Jewellers, Dallas.
A7 Ivy Williger.
A8 Pride, Texas.
A9 Bobby Ewing.
A10 The Capital Cab Company.
A11 Approximately 600 acres of land.
A12 A shopping centre.
A13 Mimosa Park.
A14 His spleen.
A15 Mr David.

B1 Burn it.
B2 Detective Ratigan.
B3 Afton Cooper.
B4 A key to a deposit box.
B5 Tom Mallory I.
B6 Alex Barton, played by Michael Wilding.
B7 Pamela.
B8 Harrison Van Buren II.
B9 James Robert Beaumont.
B10 Carter McKay and Tracey Lawton.
B11 Her son, James Beaumont.
B12 To his father, JR Ewing.
B13 He gave the evidence that his name was James Robert (JR).
B14 Carter McKay with a TV crew accusing the Ewings of sinking his oil tanker.
B15 The Faraway Hill.

C1 He asked if he should call Cally "Mum".
C2 Europe.
C3 Christopher and John Ross Ewing.
C4 London.
C5 Mrs Don Lockwood.
C6 Lady Jessica Montford.
C7 London, England.
C8 "Austin Today".
C9 A Russian doll.
C10 555–2654.
C11 The Marian Club.
C12 April Oil.
C13 She bought them in secret for Bobby Ewing.
C14 Pride, Texas.
C15 Kendell Chapman, the Ewing oil receptionist.

D1 Red Garden.
D2 Clarence Melville.
D3 25 years old.
D4 Jeanne O'Brien.
D5 Sam.
D6 Stanton Drake Real Estate.
D7 Her boss, Stanton Drake.
D8 A singles bar.
D9 Blackie Callaghan.
D10 Barkley, Oklahoma.
D11 Blackie's daughter, Meg Callaghan.
D12 Beth Ann Templeton.
D13 The Oil Barons Club.
D14 "News Maker".
D15 Gordon Wickstrom.

ANSWERS

E1 Stephanie Rogers Associates, one of the biggest PR companys in Dallas.

E2 Duke Carlisle.

E3 A bit of land next to South-fork to be turned into a racetrack.

E4 Melinda Carlisle.

E5 Eugene Inagaki.

E6 Stephanie's diaries.

E7 The Lizzie Burns Show.

E8 The voting rights in West-Star.

E9 American Airlines.

E10 James got JR to sign a property settlement for Cally and gave him Cally's divorce papers.

E11 April's flat.

E12 Sheila Foley.

E13 The Royal Monceah Hotel.

E14 Odessa, Texas, and the company was called Foley-petrotech.

E15 Dr Wexler.

F1 They made a welcome back sign.

F2 Jordan Lee.

F3 A conference of all the OPEC ministers.

F4 A pencil drawing of April.

F5 Dr Wykoff.

F6 Morrisey.

F7 Anita.

F8 The Black Widow.

F9 Sheila Foley.

F10 Duke Carlisle.

F11 James' night club, worth $500,000.

F12 Sliders.

F13 Mark Harris, played by Patrick Duffy's son.

F14 A tattoo on his arm.

F15 Mark Harris, the young cyclist.

G1 A course of drug therapy.

G2 Sly Lovegrove.

G3 Sly put an ad. in a Dallas newspaper.

G4 JR sacked Sly Lovegrove.

G5 Keller Goldman, Ryan Donia and Delgreco.

G6 Jordan was shot by one of Sheila's men, for trying to contact JR.

G7 A motorbike repair shop called Alex's.

G8 Sly kept records of everything she had ever worked on for JR at Ewing Oil.

G9 Hilary Taylor.

G10 In a mental home in Texas.

G11 In Paris.

G12 Lee Ann Nelson.

G13 James announced that Cally was pregnant.

G14 Control.

G15 Johnny Danzig.

Twin Peaks

A1 Philadelphia.
A2 1127 Hillcrescent Avenue, Philadelphia.
A3 10th October 1989.
A4 Troy.
A5 "That's a damn fine cup of coffee".
A6 Pete Martell.
A7 Lucy Moran.
A8 Packard Mill.
A9 Madeleine Ferguson or Maddy.
A10 Miss Twin Peaks.
A11 Betty Briggs.
A12 The Great Northern Hotel.
A13 Ben Horne.
A14 Diane.
A15 Via a small tape recorder.

B1 Ronette Pulaski.
B2 Johnny Horne.
B3 Margaret.
B4 The Double R Diner.
B5 Norma Jennings.
B6 Cherry pie.
B7 17 years old.
B8 Dr Lawrence Jacoby.
B9 Harold Smith.
B10 Hornes Department Store.
B11 *Flesh World*.
B12 A petrol station.
B13 Five miles south of the Canadian border.
B14 51,201, or a few less after the murders.
B15 Donna Hayward.

Knots Landing

A1 Karen and Mac McKenzie.
A2 18th November 1984.
A3 22229 Seaview circle.
A4 Shoplifting and attempted murder.
A5 Peter Hollister.
A6 Sylvia Lean.
A7 Paul Galverston.
A8 Scooter Warren.
A9 Jane.
A10 Jill Bennett.
A11 Lotus Point.
A12 15 years old.
A13 Earl Trent.
A14 Judy Trent.
A15 Paige Mattherson.

B1 That Paige wasn't his daughter, but Greg Sumners'.
B2 Olivia Cunningham.
B3 Abby Ewing.
B4 Sylvia Lean.
B5 Gary Ewing.
B6 8lb 3oz.
B7 Margaret or Meg.
B8 Peter Hollister.
B9 Long Island.
B10 By golfing buggy.
B11 Guma.
B12 1464 Heddon Valley Road, Knots Landing, CA 90745.
B13 South American.
B14 Marsha.
B15 They had a special dinner at Lotus Point.

C1 Ray Geary.
C2 A job as a TV evangelist.
C3 Pacific World Cable.
C4 Frank Elliot.
C5 A global spying centre.
C6 Toxic waste.
C7 Half of Empire Valley –
25,000 acres.
C8 Gary blew up the complex.
C9 Reverend Kathran.
C10 A home for special children,
St Agnes and the missing
persons fund.
C11 "A Better Tomorrow".
C12 Eric Fairgate.
C13 1967.
C14 Dr Russelman.
C15 Murphy.

E1 Her own suicide.
E2 Irish.
E3 With the McKenzies.
E4 St Agnes.
E5 Richard Avery, her ex-
husband.
E6 Carlos.
E7 Val Gibson and Gary Ewing.
E8 She went to Minnesota.
E9 A brain tumour.
E10 Mac McKenzie.
E11 Richard had a restaurant in
Bucks County.
E12 He threw his belongings into
the swimming pool.
E13 Peter Hollister's ashes.
E14 Because Peter always
wanted to be the centre of
attention.
E15 Budweizer.

D1 Pittsburgh 1948.
D2 State Senator of California.
D3 John Coblenz.
D4 June 1979.
D5 Five.
D6 18th November 1984.
D7 Ocean Park Hospital.
D8 8 October 1985.
D9 Charles Scott, played by
Michael York.
D10 Johnny Rourke.
D11 Frank and Patricia
Williams.
D12 Julie.
D13 Linda.
D14 Judith.
D15 Mac and Karen McKenzie.

F1 Al Baker.
F2 In his car.
F3 He was Mac's delivery man.
F4 Gary Ewing.
F5 That Gary was the twins'
father. She had thought that
Ben was their father.
F6 Jody Campbell.
F7 Abby was working at Sids
Garage when Charles walked
in.
F8 Philadelphia.
F9 On the first day of college.
F10 The Golden Valley Ball
Room.
F11 Charles Scott.
F12 Parkhill.
F13 20 years.
F14 "Mother".
F15 Lotus Point.

G1 Peggy.
G2 A camper van.
G3 To live with Al, but not marry him.
G4 Champagne, of course.
G5 She bought back his old car.
G6 Cousins.
G7 Marry him.
G8 White and off white.

G9 A surprise birthday party; Val's at home, Jill's at Lotus Point.
G10 Cup cakes.
G11 "Daddy".
G12 She threw them into the ocean.
G13 Barbara.
G14 The guitar.
G15 27,000 dollars.

Dynasty and The Colbys

A1 N3S0GT.
A2 Tracy Kendell, who was fired to make way for Krystle.
A3 Ben Carrington.
A4 Ten per cent ownership in the Colby Enterprises Corporation.
A5 Henry.
A6 Chris Deegan.
A7 Andrew Laird.
A8 Frankie.

A9 Iris Dean.
A10 Princess Elena.
A11 29th September 1957.
A12 On a boat off the coast of San Francisco.
A13 The Colby Timber Company.
A14 Rashid Ahmed.
A15 Krystle sold the emerald and diamond necklace that Blake had given her. Later Blake bought it back.

Falcon Crest

A1 Terry Ranson.
A2 Small Virtue.
A3 Stephanie Hoffman and Terry Ranson.
A4 Publisher of the *New Globe*.
A5 Melissa Gioberti.
A6 Maggie Gioberti and Richard Channing.
A7 She lost her memory.
A8 Connie Gininni.

A9 Francesca Wines.
A10 Anna Rossini and Damon Ross.
A11 To turn Falcon Crest into a theme park.
A12 Gustav Riebmann.
A13 He removed a brain tumor.
A14 Henri Denault.
A15 St Martin's Church.

The Australian Suds

Neighbours

A1 Cedric.

A2 He was named after her husband Len's brother Cedric.

A3 A dentist.

A4 Iris.

A5 Ian Chadwick.

A6 Louise Hampstead.

A7 *Dark Victory, Now Voyager* and *Casablanca*.

A8 Spare Parts.

A9 Scoop.

A10 Matt Cohen.

A11 Barry.

A12 Gold in the creek at the bottom of the garden.

A13 Karl Banks.

A14 Karl tried to electrocute Mrs Mangel in her own home.

A15 The 2nd Erinsborough Scout Troop.

C1 Bob Stanton.

C2 Keith Franklin.

C3 Pixie, Trixie and Dixie.

C4 A painting of himself.

C5 Bruce Zadro.

C6 A black eye.

C7 Henry Ramsay.

C8 Caroline.

C9 Sharon put vinegar in the cake.

C10 Henry left Madge's cake on the roof of his car, and when he braked the cake fell off.

C11 The Reverend Samson.

C12 Sharon Davies.

C13 $9,500.

C14 Mr Wembley, Year Two's maths teacher.

C15 Roland.

B1 Erinsborough Real Estates.

B2 23rd July 1988.

B3 COA 629.

B4 Derek Morris.

B5 Emphysema and pneumonia.

B6 Nick painted graffiti on a railway bridge.

B7 Gordon Hemmings.

B8 Penelope Porter.

B9 ASBO.

B10 27th July 1988.

B11 Des Clarke.

B12 $150,000.

B13 $151,000.

B14 The tip of the toy drum kit that Mike had bought him.

B15 $30 each.

D1 65,680 points.

D2 Skinner, with 68,500 points.

D3 70,500 points.

D4 Skinner was 2nd with 68,500, Ian was 3rd with 55,280 and Johnno was 4th with 52,680 points.

D5 Hiccups.

D6 Charles Spencer.

D7 St Albans, Herts.

D8 BNZ 832.

D9 Betty Bristo.

D10 She had been married three times.

D11 The Good Friends Good Neighbours competition.

D12 *Modern Family* magazine.

D13 Reflections Cosmetics.

D14 Lust perfume.

D15 Rona and Ben are Melissa's parents and Sean is her brother.

E1 Gail named them Robert (after Rob), Cameron and Lucinda.
E2 Erinsborough Community Radio.
E3 Des Clarke and Melanie Pearson.
E4 A vet's assistant.
E5 She called the possum Henry.
E6 Parkside Pacific.
E7 Mr Vasilior.
E8 Ramsay (Madge), Brown, Goodman, Bishop (Harold), and Downing.
E9 Kerry Bishop/Mangel.
E10 Australian Institute of Sport in Canberra.
E11 The 11-metres hurdles.
E12 Scott Robinson, to report on Pete's progress for the local newspaper, and Mike Young.
E13 144 litres of ice cream.
E14 An ice cream-eating contest with chopsticks.
E15 Jessie Ross.

F1 Ewan O'Brien.
F2 Linda Giles.
F3 Madeleine Price.
F4 Rachel Frazer.
F5 The ageing process.
F6 The Daniels Corporation.
F7 Josh's father runs a newsagents.
F8 Lord Ledgerwood, played by Derek Nimmo.
F9 $60,000.
F10 $5,000 to Henry, Charlene and Kerry.
F11 Japanese.
F12 Jenny Owens.
F13 Mike was protective towards Jenny because she had fallen off the back of Mike's bike.
F14 Nick won a scholarship to London.

G1 Rob died in a car crash.
G2 Tasmania.
G3 Gary Head.
G4 A trail bike.
G5 Boof made Todd break into a scrapyard to get a part for his bike.
G6 Jonathon Whiting.
G7 Arthur Lancing.
G8 Derek Wilcox.
G9 New Zealand.
G10 Matt Williams.
G11 Hilary Robinson.
G12 Mary Combi.
G13 The Butterfly Sanctuary at the local zoo.
G14 In New Zealand, where they were both working.
G15 Robyn Taylor.

Home and Away

A1 Eric.

A2 Dag Dog.

A3 A road repairer.

A4 Sydney.

A5 Fisher expelled them from the school cadet corps.

A6 Steven Matherson.

A7 The Summer Bay Rollers.

A8 Ruth Stewart.

A9 Pippa thought she looked fat because she was pregnant.

A10 Floss and Neville.

A11 Carly Morris.

A12 Floss reads the tarot cards.

A13 Mark Williams and Karen Boddington.

A14 10th June 1987.

A15 Staying with a friend.

C1 Image.

C2 Jonathan Coleman.

C3 "Santa doesn't come to Summer Bay".

C4 Leanne.

C5 Alf Stewart.

C6 Alf and Donald are brothers-in-law.

C7 Marilyn became a quiz show hostess.

C8 Ernie Jacobs.

C9 Troy and Justin.

C10 Murray Jenson.

C11 Lorraine.

C12 He played in a country and western band.

C13 "There's a hole in my bucket".

C14 Murray spends all his time fishing.

C15 Al Simpson played by Terry Donovan (Jason's dad).

B1 Chris Reynolds and Geoff Limes.

B2 The Bay Side Diner.

B3 Ailsa Stewart and Bobby Fisher (or Simpson).

B4 The *Summer Bay Courier*.

B5 Bobby won the student of the year award 1988.

B6 Alan Fisher.

B7 Summer Bay District High School.

B8 Martha.

B9 Rex Wilson.

B10 Jewellery.

B11 Jeff Cousak.

B12 $500.

B13 Pug.

B14 Morag Bellingham and Donald Fisher.

B15 Samantha Morris.

D1 Banjo.

D2 Macklin Developments.

D3 Chickens or chucks as they are called in Australia.

D4 Alzheimer's disease.

D5 Chambers.

D6 In the army.

D7 A tank.

D8 The army.

D9 Vince.

D10 Coastal Video Hire.

D11 Ellen Morris.

D12 A brooch that had been her mother's.

D13 $11.500.

D14 The company was Graham and Winters, and the lawyer was Mr Hadley.

D15 Sophie Simpson.

E1 Pippa and Tom.

E2 Marilyn.

E3 Lance Smart.

E4 Steven, Sophie and Bobby.

E5 Football practice.

E6 Ben and Grant.

E7 Steven tried to give Tom the kiss of life.

E8 Alf Stewart.

E9 Picnicport Road just after the Bay Road turn-off.

E10 Ailsa Stewart.

E11 Pippa tried to behave as if nothing had happened.

E12 Working for Macklins in New York.

E13 A stroke.

E14 Viv.

E15 Ailsa's sister, Bridget Jackson.

F1 Dodge.

F2 In Celia Stewart's shop fire, where he had the flat.

F3 Dodge.

F4 Steven.

F5 To get Paul Jenson to play the piano in public.

F6 Sophie Simpson.

F7 Adam Cameron with the help of Marilyn.

F8 Vicki Baxter.

F9 Pippa was trying to park in the same place that Ben was trying to park. They had a row.

F10 Summer Bay 993000.

F11 Karen Dean.

F12 Marilyn Chambers.

F13 Karen's brother Blake.

F14 Bobby.

F15 Daniel.

G1 Jennifer is Alf's cousin.

G2 Daniel was an art critic.

G3 Hazel Lime.

G4 A father for Bobbys baby.

G5 Alan Stone.

G6 Godzilla films.

G7 The brooch fell off Carly's coat into a box that Ben took to the rubbish dump and Adam found it.

G8 Mr Kennedy.

G9 Surf Patrol Life Guard.

G10 Marilyn and Adam, Ben and Carly, and Bobby and Geoff.

G11 Wendy and Susan Reynolds.

G12 He used to lock them in a cupboard under the stairs.

G13 Megan Williams Tierney.

G14 Helen Wakefield.

G15 A family Bible.

Prisoner Cell Block H

A1 Acting Chief Prison Officer.
A2 Prison Officer and Union Rep.
A3 The Governor at Barnhurst Prison.
A4 A pet rock, which Vera threw away.
A5 Jack Smith.
A6 Cancer.
A7 Leila.
A8 Agnes Foster.
A9 Bill Jackson.
A10 Chrissie Latham. She stabbed him during a prison riot.
A11 Gordon Humphrey.
A12 Maria Desmond.
A13 Ted Douglas (played by Ian Smith – Harold Bishop from *Neighbours*).
A14 Wendy Scott.
A15 Peter Hope.

B1 The Freak.
B2 Alison Page.
B3 Kerry Vincent.
B4 Kevin Burns.
B5 Marne.
B6 Tennyson.
B7 Officer Jock Stewart.
B8 She escaped and became a hooker.
B9 Gail Summers.
B10 Drove a taxi.
B11 Suzi Driscoll.
B12 Barnhurst.
B13 Mrs O'Reagan.
B14 Terry Harrison.
B15 Terry Harrison.

The Flying Doctors

A1 Rick Mansell and Alan Dogherty.
A2 Neil Hutton.
A3 Penny Armstrong.
A4 The radiographer at the hospital.
A5 David Hutton.
A6 Rick Mansell, one of the boys George Baxter adopted for a week.
A7 The call sign is Zulu Yankie Gulf.
A8 The call sign is Mike Sierra Foxtrot.
A9 The call sign is Victor Charlie Charlie.
A10 Gladys.
A11 Broken Hill.
A12 Edward (Teddy) Faithful.
A13 Jenny Rose (played by Elaine Smith – Daphne from *Neighbours*).
A14 Douggie Kennedy.
A15 *The Guinness Book of Records* for the fastest time for one man to put a car engine together.

The Satellite Soaps

A1 Henderson.
A2 Forester Creations.
A3 Phillip.
A4 Jobot Cosmetics.
A5 Esther.
A6 Newman Towers.
A7 Four: Ridge, Thorn, Kristen and Floatchia.
A8 Genoa City.

A9 Michael Crawford.
A10 Peter Flint.
A11 Gina Demont.
A12 Sister Scott.
A13 Bay City.
A14 Joanna Gardner, Barron Tate, Vincent Tourneur.
A15 Brick Wallace.

For Soap Experts Only

A1 The motel cleaner, Amy Turtle.
A2 Minnie Caldwell.
A3 Pam Ewing with Bobby James Ewing.
A4 £4 per hour.
A5 Meadowcroft.
A6 Milk.
A7 Bill Conti.
A8 "Davo".
A9 Arkenfield Stables.

A10 The House of Howard.
A11 Jupiter Moon.
A13 Minyip.
A14 The Summer Bay Liquor Store, the Boat Hire service, the Summer Bay Caravan Park and the Yacht broker-age.
A15 19th February 1985, with over 12 million.